Contents

Highlights®
Puzzle Buzz®
Can you find this
buzzing bee?
It is hiding 3 times
on the cover.

COVER ILLUSTRATION BY CATHI MINGUS

W9-CFD-932

Snow Maze

START

Help Ozzie race down the hill. Find a path from START to FINISH. If something is in the way, choose a different path.

Hidden Pictures

Can you find these 13 items hidden in this picture?

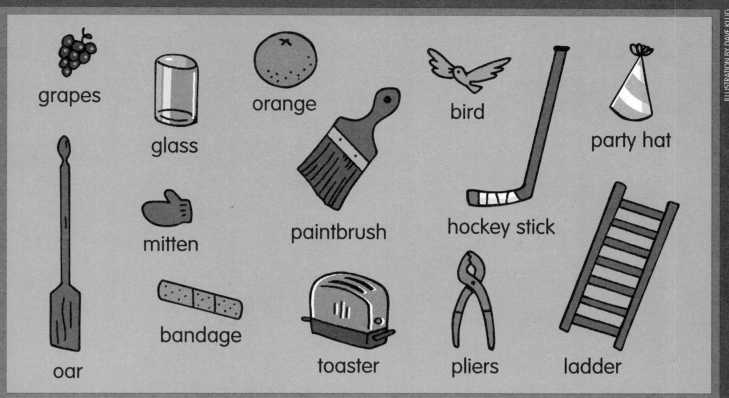

grapes

glass

orange

bird

party hat

mitten

paintbrush

hockey stick

oar

bandage

toaster

pliers

ladder

Dot to Dot

Connect the dots from 1 to 33 to see what this book is about.

Fish Search

What can you see beneath the ocean? You can see lots and lots of fish. Can you find all 15?

Can you find?

Two of the fish are the same. Can you find them?

ILLUSTRATION BY DONNA CATANESE

7

Answer on page 30

Double Scoops

Time for ice cream! These two pictures are a bit different. Add your stickers to the picture on this page to make them match.

44 FLAVORS

9

Answer on page 31

Wiggle Pictures

These insects have been twisted and turned.
Can you figure out what each one is?

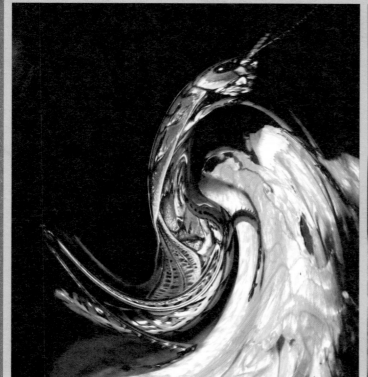

Answer on page 31

Art Starters

Fill-in Fun Color each space that has a dot to see an animal.

Color Copy Use crayons or markers to a make a robot that matche

ILLUSTRATION BY RON ZALME

Step by Step Follow the steps to draw a jet plane.

1.

2.

3.

4.

5.

13

Match Maker

Every snazzy sock in the picture has one that looks just like it. Find all 10 matching pairs.

Answer on page 31

What's Wrong?®

6. What instrument is this girl playing?
- flute
- trombone
- tuba

7. How many eggs are there in two dozen?

8. All dinosaurs were big.
- True
- False

9. Name five things you find in a tool kit.

10. In what state will you find the Liberty Bell?
- Iowa
- Ohio
- Pennsylvania

ILLUSTRATION BY KELLY KENNEDY

Ready, Set, Bowl!

START

Roll the ball from START to FINISH. After you finish, count how many bowling pins there are in the whole picture.

FINISH

Answer on page 32

Countdown

Find 5 ⚒ 4 🧁 3 🪣 2 🌙 1 🐕

23

Answer on page 32

Helping Hands

Car Find

There are 16 car words hidden in the letters. Some words are across. Others are up and down. We found HEADLIGHT. Can you find the rest?

Word List

AIR BAG
BRAKES
BUMPER
CAR
DASHBOARD
DRIVE
ENGINE
GASOLINE
~~HEADLIGHT~~
HOOD
HORN
SEAT BELT
TIRE
TRUNK
WHEEL
WINDSHIELD

```
W  H  E  E  L  C  A  R  H  G
I  O  X  T  R  U  N  K  O  A
N  O  Q  B  U  M  P  E  R  S
D  D  R  I  V  E  F  J  N  O
S  E  A  T  B  E  L  T  Z  L
H  E  A  D  L  I  G  H  T  I
I  X  A  I  R  B  A  G  Q  N
E  T  I  R  E  N  G  I  N  E
L  Q  B  R  A  K  E  S  X  Y
D  A  S  H  B  O  A  R  D  Z
```

Wheel Deal Draw your favorite kind of car on this road.

C Is For ?

Tongue Twister

Try to say this three times as fast as you can: **Can you can a can as a canner can can a can?**

ILLUSTRATION BY DAVE KLUG

Answers

Cover

2. Snow Maze

Two of a Kind

4. Hidden Pictures®

5. Dot to Dot

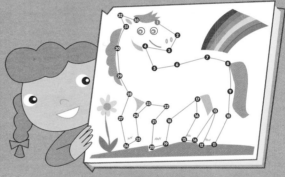

6. Fish Search

The two fish shaded blue are the same.

Highlights Puzzle BuZz

Answers

8. Double Scoops

10. Wiggle Pictures

ladybug

grasshopper

bee

caterpillar

butterfly

dragonfly

12. Fill-in Fun

It's a panda!

14. Match Maker

16. What's Wrong?®

Here are the things we found. You may have found others.

18. Try 10

1. Orange, grape, cranberry, and apple
   Did you think of others?
2. Circle the baseball—the ball at the top.
3. A tiger has stripes.
4. True
5. Circle the red and blue cans.
6. She is playing a trombone.
7. There are 24 eggs in two dozen.
8. False
9. Hammer, saw, nails, screwdriver, safety goggles
10. Pennsylvania

Answers

20. Ready, Set, Bowl!

There are 36 bowling pins.

22. Countdown

24. Helping Hands

26. Car Find

```
W H E E L C A R H G
I O X T R U N K O A
N O Q B U M P E R S
D R I V E F J N O
S E A T B E L T Z L
H E A D L I G H T I
I X A I R B A G Q N
E T I R E N G I N E
L Q B R A K E S X Y
D A S H B O A R D Z
```

28. C Is For ?

Here are the C words we found.
You may have found others.

1. cat	12. crown	23. cowboy
2. cattails	13. coin	24. candle
3. car	14. crib	25. castle
4. cow	15. crane	26. compass
5. cup	16. cap	27. crab
6. cane	17. carrots	28. cracker
7. cub	18. cactus	29. camel
8. cake	19. camper	30. clown
9. coat	20. crayons	31. cricket
10. corn	21. canoe	32. caterpillar
11. cage	22. cookie	33. calculator

What Is It?

It's a woodchuck!

32